Primary Skills
Maths 5-6

Sarah Lindsay

This book belongs to:

_____

WHSmith

What your child will learn from this book

This book will help your child cover these areas of maths:

- Learning to read and write numbers to 20
- Adding and taking away to 10
- Tens and units
- Counting in steps of 2, 3, 4, and 5
- A half and a quarter
- Starting to tell the time
- Recognising shapes

How you can help

A few simple guidelines will ensure that your child gets the best from this book:

- Make sure that you explain what the book is about.

- Do a few examples on a page with your child to ensure she or he understands.

- Encourage your child to do all the exercises on a page but don't expect too much to be done at a time.

- Ensure you understand what your child gets right and wrong. Explain any difficulties and try to provide more practice.

- Give all the praise and encouragement you can.

Page 3 explains how to use this book.

How to use this book

- The book is set out in straightforward two page units. Each unit contains teaching points, exercises and a special challenge:

The Teaching Box explains new learning simply and directly.

The Exercises provide lots of practice to ensure the learning is fully understood.

The Challenge Star at the end of the unit extends your child's skills still further.

- Throughout the book you will also find regular special checking pages:

Check ups These appear after every few units and give your child a chance to recall what has been covered.

Test yourself This comes at the end and tests everything covered in the book.

Read and write numbers to 5

1 2 3 4 5

1. **a** Colour 3 fish.

   b Colour 2 fish.

   c Colour 4 fish.

2. How many fish are in each bowl?

   a

   _3_

   b

   _2_

   c

   _4_

   d

   _5_

   ✓ v. Good

3. Put a red circle around each number 3.
Put a blue circle around each number 4.

4   2   3   2   1

3   1   4   3

2   5   3   5

V. Good

4. Draw the fish.

    a 3 fish   **b** 4 fish   **c** 2 fish

5. Put a circle around each set of 5 fish.

V. Good

5

Ordering numbers to 5

Look at the numbers.

They go up in order.

1. Join the dots to make 4 shapes. Start on 1 each time.

a

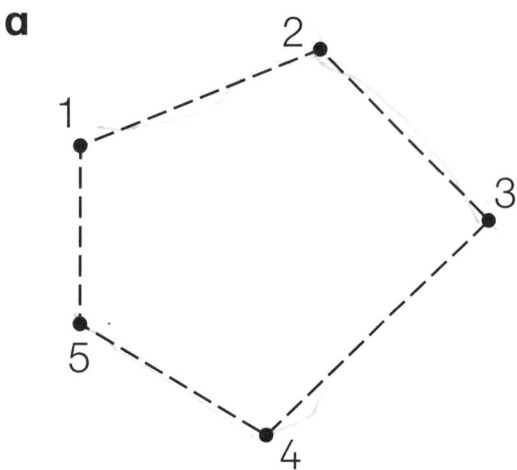

b

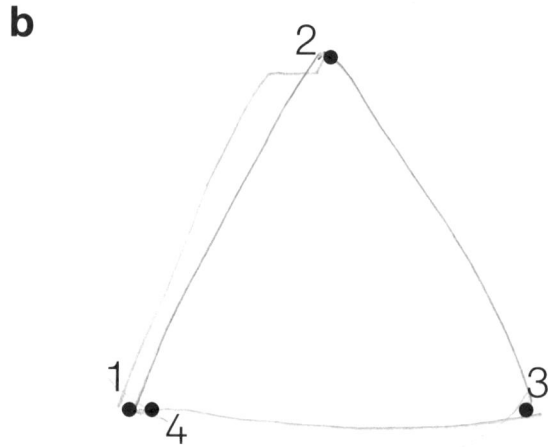

c

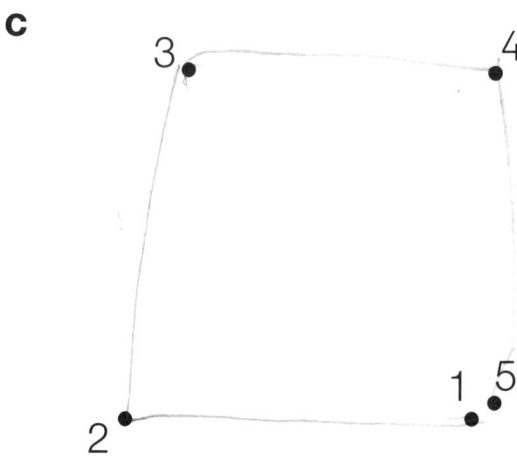

d

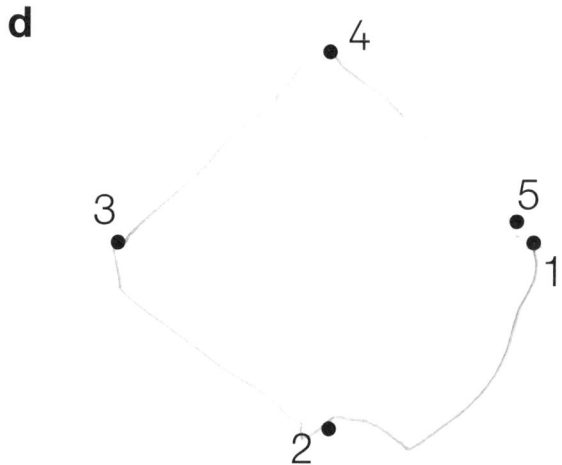

2. Fill in the missing numbers.

a 1 2 __3__ 4 5

b 1 2 3 __4__ 5

c __1__ 2 3 __4__

d __1__ 2 3 4 __5__

3. When we are counting, which number comes first?

a 2 or 1? __1__

b 3 or 4? __3__

c 3 or 2? __2__

d 5 or 3? __3__

e 4 or 2? __2__

f 1 or 4? __1__

4.

| 1 | 2 | 3 | 4 | 5 |

Look at the number line.

a Which number comes after 3? __4__

b Which number comes before 2? __1__

c Which number comes after 4? __5__

Addition to 5

We can add numbers together like this ....

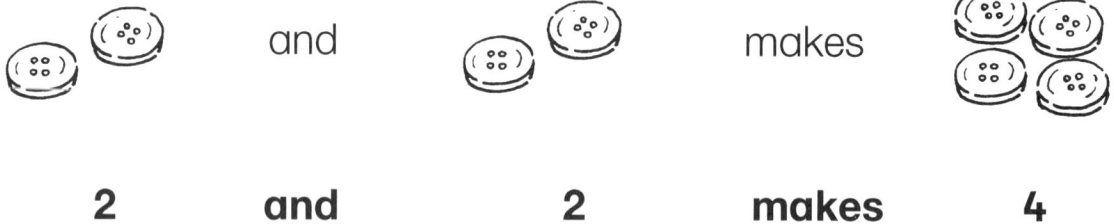

2   **and**   2   **makes**   4

1. Write the missing number in each gap.

a   and   makes   **3**

b   and   makes   5

c   and   makes

Now we will use the right signs ... **+** and **=**.

d   +   =   5

e   +   =   5

Well done Nathanael

2. Write the numbers in the gaps.

a   [buttons]   and   [buttons]   makes   [buttons]

$$\underline{\hspace{1cm}}\;2\;\underline{\hspace{1cm}} + \underline{\hspace{1cm}}\;3\;\underline{\hspace{1cm}} = \underline{\hspace{1cm}}\;5\;\underline{\hspace{1cm}}$$

b   [button]   and   [buttons]   makes   [buttons]

$$\underline{\;1\;} + \underline{\;3\;} = \underline{\;4\;}$$

c   [buttons]   and   [buttons]   makes   [buttons]

$$\underline{\;3\;} + \underline{\;2\;} = \underline{\;5\;}$$

d   [buttons]   and   [button]   makes   [buttons]

$$\underline{\;4\;} + \underline{\;1\;} = \underline{\;5\;}$$

Well done
Nathanael

3. Do these sums.

a $2 + 2 = \underline{\;4\;}$ **b** $4 + 1 = \underline{\;5\;}$

c $3 + 1 = \underline{\;4\;}$ **d** $0 + 3 = \underline{\;3\;}$

e $3 + 2 = \underline{\;5\;}$ **f** $2 + 1 = \underline{\;3\;}$

g $1 + 4 = \underline{\;5\;}$ **h** $5 + 0 = \underline{\;5\;}$

Very Good
Nathanael

Subtraction to 5

Sam has 3 bones.

He hides 2.

Sam has 1 bone left.

1. If you take away 2 bones from Sam how many will he have left?

a _2_

b _3_

c _0_

Now take away 3 bones.

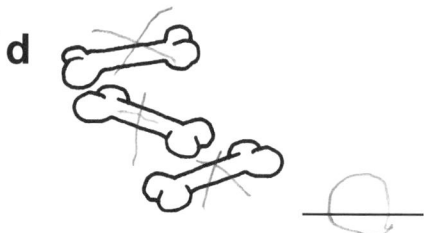

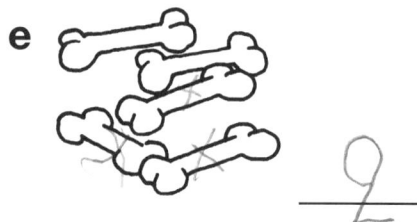

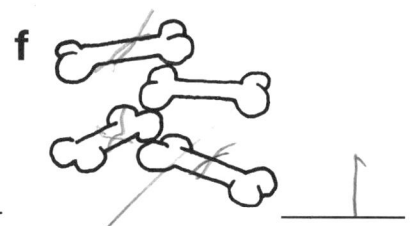

d _0_

e _2_

f _1_

10

We write take away sums like this ...

 take away 2 is

3 − 2 = 1

*− means **take away***

2. Write the answers.

a − 2 = ___ 1

b − 1 = ___ 1

c 4 − 2 = ___ 2

d 5 − 3 = ___ 2

e 2 − 2 = ___ 0

Very Good
Nathanael
✓

f 3 − 1 = ___ 2

3. Write the answers.

a 5 take away 3 is ___ 2 .

b Sam has 4 bones. He hides 1.
How many bones does Sam have left? ___ 3

c 5 take away 4 is ___ 1 .

d Sam has 5 bones. He hides 3.
How many bones does Sam have left? ___ 2

Very Good
Nathanael
✓

11

Knowing when to add or subtract to 5

> Remember ...
> **+** means **add**
> **–** means **take away**

1. Answer these sums.

a $2 + 2 = \underline{4}$ ✓

b $3 - 1 = \underline{2}$ ✓

c $5 - 3 = \underline{2}$ ✓

d $4 + 1 = \underline{5}$ ✓

e $1 + 1 = \underline{2}$ ✓

f $3 - 2 = \underline{1}$ ✓

V. Good
Dalianael

2. Which sign, **+** or **–**, makes these sums right? Fill in the gaps.

a $3 \underline{-} 1 = 2$

b $4 \underline{} 1 = 5$

c $3 \underline{} 1 = 4$

d $3 \underline{} 2 = 1$

e $5 \underline{} 0 = 5$

f $4 \underline{} 1 = 3$

3. Which sign would you use?

Fill in the gaps with **+** or **−**.

a 3   add   2   =   5

    3   _____   2   =   5

b 4   subtract   1   =   3

    4   _____   1   =   3

c 5   less   4   =   1

    5   _____   4   =   1

d 4   and   1 more   =   5

    4   _____   1   =   5

e 3   take away   2   =   1

    3   _____   2   =   1

4. Put the right sign in the gap.

a 5p _____ 2p = 3p

b 4p _____ 1p = 5p

c 3p _____ 3p = 0p

d 2p _____ 3p = 5p

First or last, more or less (1)

When something comes **first** it is at the beginning.

When something is **last** it is at the end.

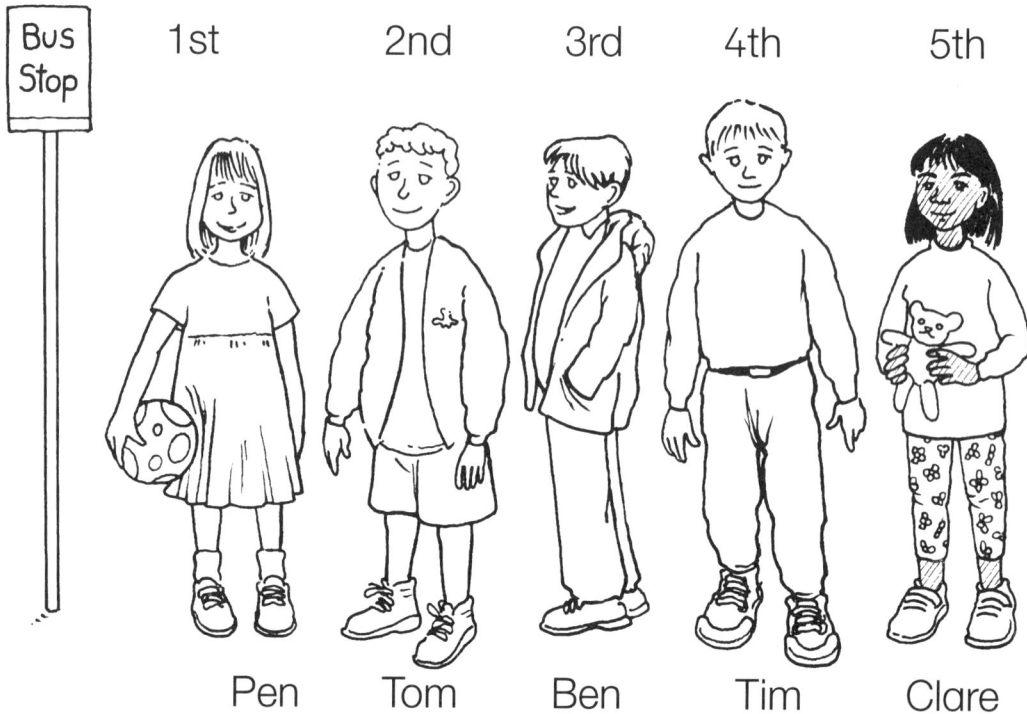

Bus Stop	1st	2nd	3rd	4th	5th
	Pen	Tom	Ben	Tim	Clare

1. Look at the picture. Answer the questions.

a Who is first? ____Pen____

b Who is last? ____To hm____

c Who is 2nd? ____B e____

d Who is 4th? _____

e Who is 1st? _____

f Who is 3rd? _____

As numbers go up they are one more than the one before.

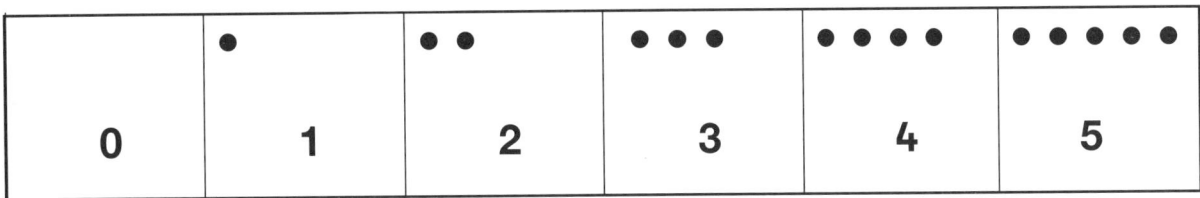

0	1	2	3	4	5
	•	• •	• • •	• • • •	• • • • •

2. Look at the number line. Answer the questions.

a Which number is more than 4? _____

b Which two numbers are less than 2? _____ _____

c Which two numbers are more than 3? _____ _____

d Which four numbers are less than 4? _____ _____ _____

_____

3. Fill in the gaps.

a	b	c	d	e

a The 1st letter is _____ .

b The 4th letter is _____ .

c The last and 5th letter is _____ .

d The 2nd letter is _____ .

e The middle letter is _____ .

Adding to make 5

> Look at how many ways I can make 4.
>
> $$0 + 4 = 4$$
>
> $$1 + 3 = 4$$
>
> $$2 + 2 = 4$$
>
> $$3 + 1 = 4$$
>
> $$4 + 0 = 4$$

1. How many different ways can you make 3?

$$0 \quad + \quad 3 \quad = \quad 3$$

$$1 \quad + \quad \underline{2} \quad = \quad 3$$

$$2 \quad + \quad \underline{} \quad = \quad 3$$

$$3 \quad + \quad \underline{} \quad = \quad 3$$

2. How many different ways can you make 5?

$$\underline{0} \quad + \quad 5 \quad = \quad 5 \qquad \underline{0} \quad + \quad \underline{5} \quad = \quad 5$$

$$\underline{1} \quad + \quad 4 \quad = \quad 5 \qquad \underline{} \quad + \quad \underline{4} \quad = \quad 5$$

$$\underline{2} \quad + \quad 3 \quad = \quad 5 \qquad \underline{} \quad + \quad \underline{3} \quad = \quad 5$$

3. Do these sums.

$0 + 0 = 0$

$1 + 1 = \underline{\hspace{2cm}}$

$2 + 2 = \underline{\hspace{2cm}}$

The answer goes up 2 each time.

4. Check the answers.

✔ = right   ✗ = wrong

a $2 + 3 = 4$ __✗__

b $3 + 1 = 5$ _____

c $3 + 1 = 4$ _____

d $2 + 2 = 4$ _____

e $2 + 1 = 3$ _____

f $5 + 0 = 5$ _____

g $3 + 2 = 3$ _____

h $2 + 1 = 4$ _____

5. Answer these questions.

a Tuhil had 5 sweets. He ate 3.

How many were left? __2__

b 2 fish were in Tom's net. 2 jumped out.

How many were left? __0__

c 2 dogs were playing. 1 ran off.

How many were left? __1__

17

2D shapes

 **square**

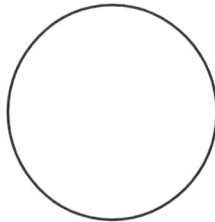 **circle**

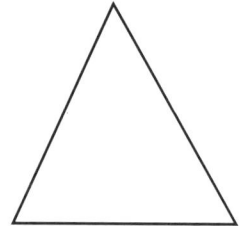 **triangle**

A ○ has a **curved** side.

The □ and △ have **straight sides**.

1. Draw over these shapes. Answer the questions.

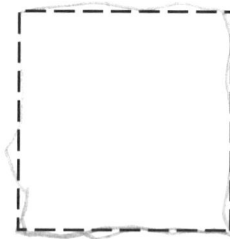

a How many sides? _____ sides

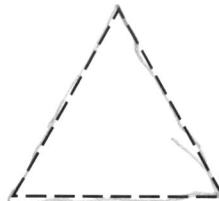

b How many sides? _____ sides

2. Colour the shapes.

a 4 sides – blue

b 3 sides – green

c circles – yellow

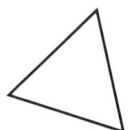

3. Draw a ...

square

triangle

circle

4. Draw the missing shape in the gap.

a A _____ has 3 sides.

b A _____ has a curved side.

c A _____ and a _____ have straight sides.

d A _____ has 4 sides.

5. How many shapes can you find on the cat?

a _____ circles

b _____ squares

c _____ triangles

Patterns

A **pattern** can happen again and again, like this ...

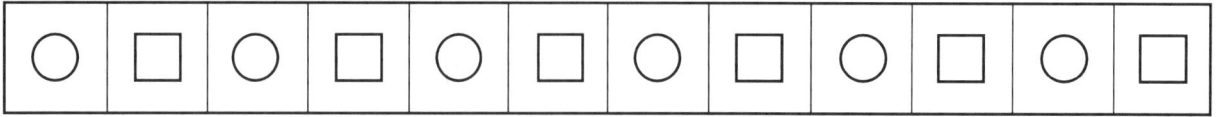

○	□	○	□	○	□	○	□	○	□	○	□

1. Finish these patterns.

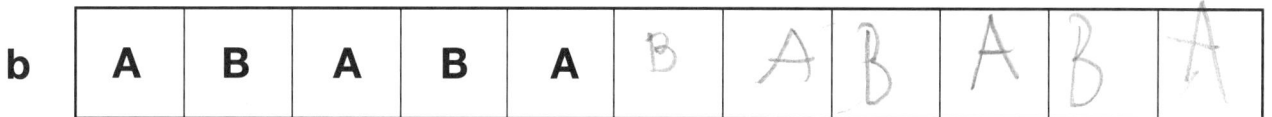

a

✗	○	✗	○	✗	O	X	O	X	O	X

b

A	B	A	B	A	B	A	B	A	B	A

c

●	○	●	○	●	○	●	○	●	○	●

d

☺	☹	☺	☹	☺	☹	☺	☹	☺	☹	☺

2. Fill in the gaps.

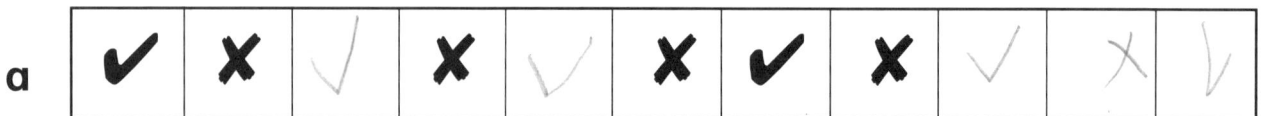

a

✔	✗	✓	✗	✓	✗	✔	✗	✓	✗	✓

b

△	○	△	○	△	○	△	○	△	○	△

c

4	3	4	3	4	3	4	3	4	3	4

3. Now try these. Look carefully at each pattern.

a

b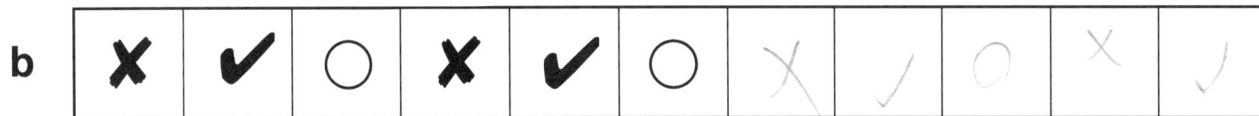

c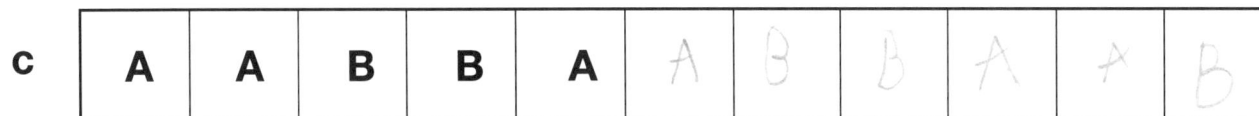

d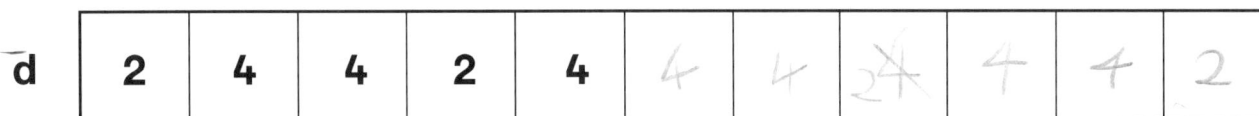

e

f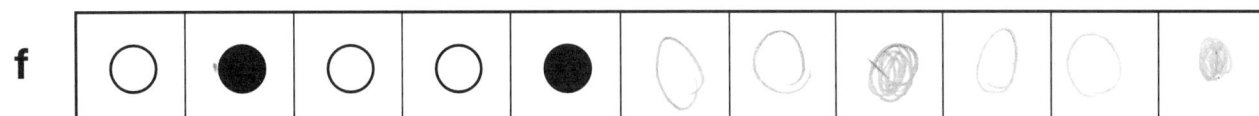

g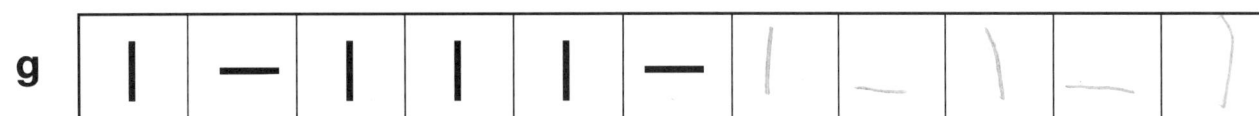

4. Make some patterns of your own.

a Use △ and □.

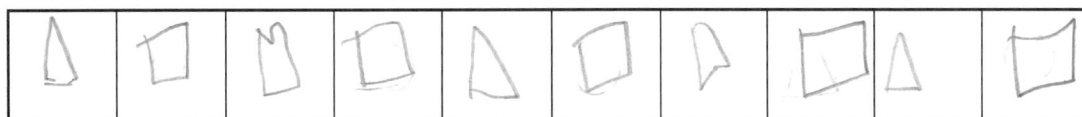

b Use ✔ and ✘.

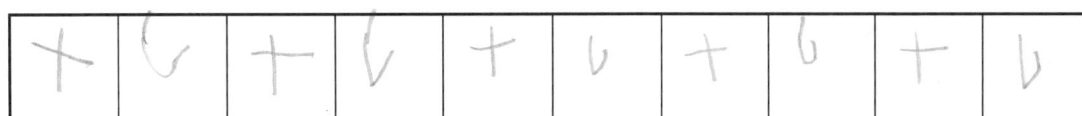

Time – days and months

1. Put the pictures in the right order.

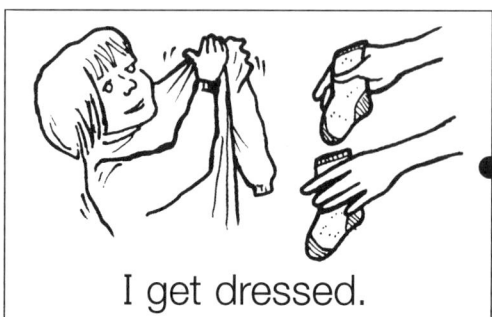

I go to bed.	**1** — **I get up**
I go home	**2** — _____
I get up.	**3** — _____
I go to school.	**4** — _____
I get dressed.	**5** — _____

2. Put the days of the week in order.

Tuesday
Sunday
Wednesday
Saturday
Friday
Thursday
Monday

1 **Sunday** _____ 2 _____ 3 **Tuesday** _____

4 _____ 5 **Thursday** _____ 6 _____

7 _____

3. Write March, June and April in the right gaps.

1	January	2	February	3	*ok est*
4		5	May	6	
7	July	8	August	9	September
10	October	11	November	12	December

4. Answer these questions.

a In which month is your birthday? _____

b In which month is Christmas? _____

c Which day do you like best? _____

Check-up 1

1. **a** Colour 3 apples.

   b How many oranges? _____

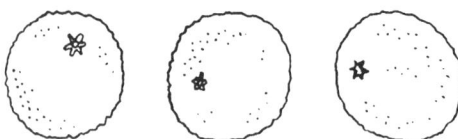

2. Fill in the missing number.

   a 1 2 3 _____ 5

   b 2 _____ 4

3. Do these sums.

   a $3 + 2 =$ _____

   b $2 + 1 =$ _____

4. Do these sums.

   a $5 - 2 =$ _____

   b $3 - 2 =$ _____

5. Put the right sign in the gap.

   a 4 _____ $2 = 2$

   b 5 _____ $0 = 5$

6.

| 1 | 2 | 3 | 4 | 5 |

   a Which number is more than 4? _____

   b Which number is less than 2? _____

7. How many different ways can you make 3?

_____ + _____ = 3   _____ + _____ = 3

_____ + _____ = 3   _____ + _____ = 3

8. **a** Draw a square in the box.
Write how many sides.

b Draw a triangle in the box.
Write how many sides.

_____ sides   _____ sides

9. Finish the pattern.

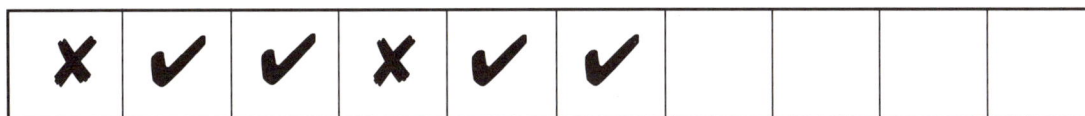

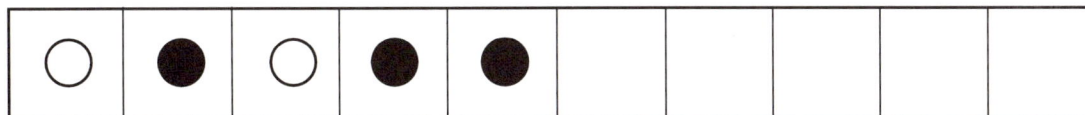

✗	✔	✔	✗	✔	✔				

○	●	○	●	●					

10.

Who came first? PEN

Who came last? BEN

Read and write numbers to 10

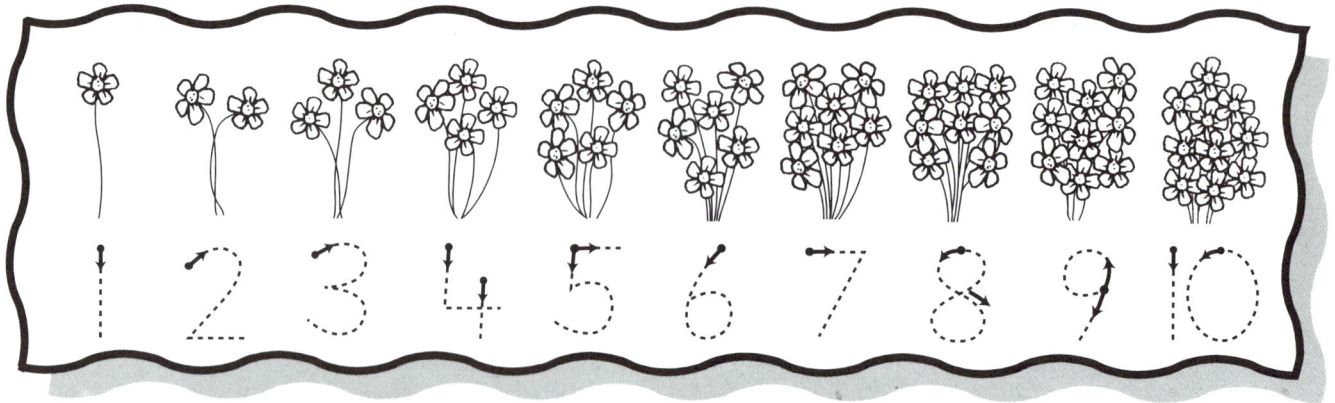

1 2 3 4 5 6 7 8 9 10

1. a Colour 6 flowers.

b Colour 8 flowers.

c Colour 2 flowers.

2. How many flowers?

a

b _____

c _____

d _____

3. Put a red circle around each number 8.
Put a green circle around each number 7.
Put a blue circle around each number 9.

7   2   5   9   4   5
                                 7
8   1   10   8   2
                         3   8
6   9   6   6   8
2   3   7   7   9

4. Draw the flowers.

a 5 flowers   **b** 8 flowers   **c** 6 flowers

5. Put a circle around the bunches with 7 flowers.

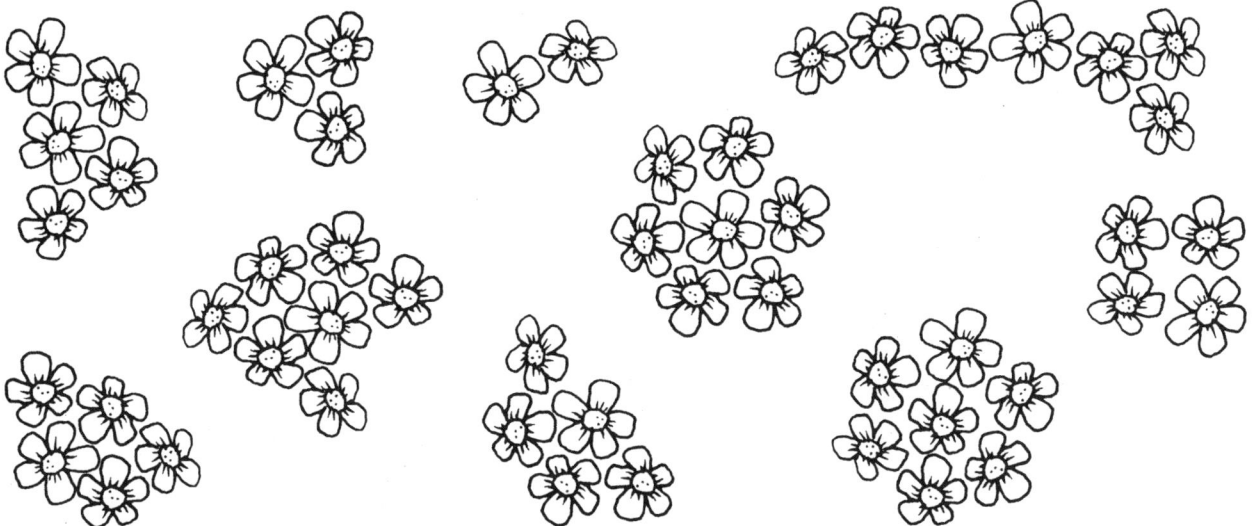

Ordering numbers to 10

Look at the numbers. They go up in order.

1. Join the dots to make the shapes. Start on 1 each time.

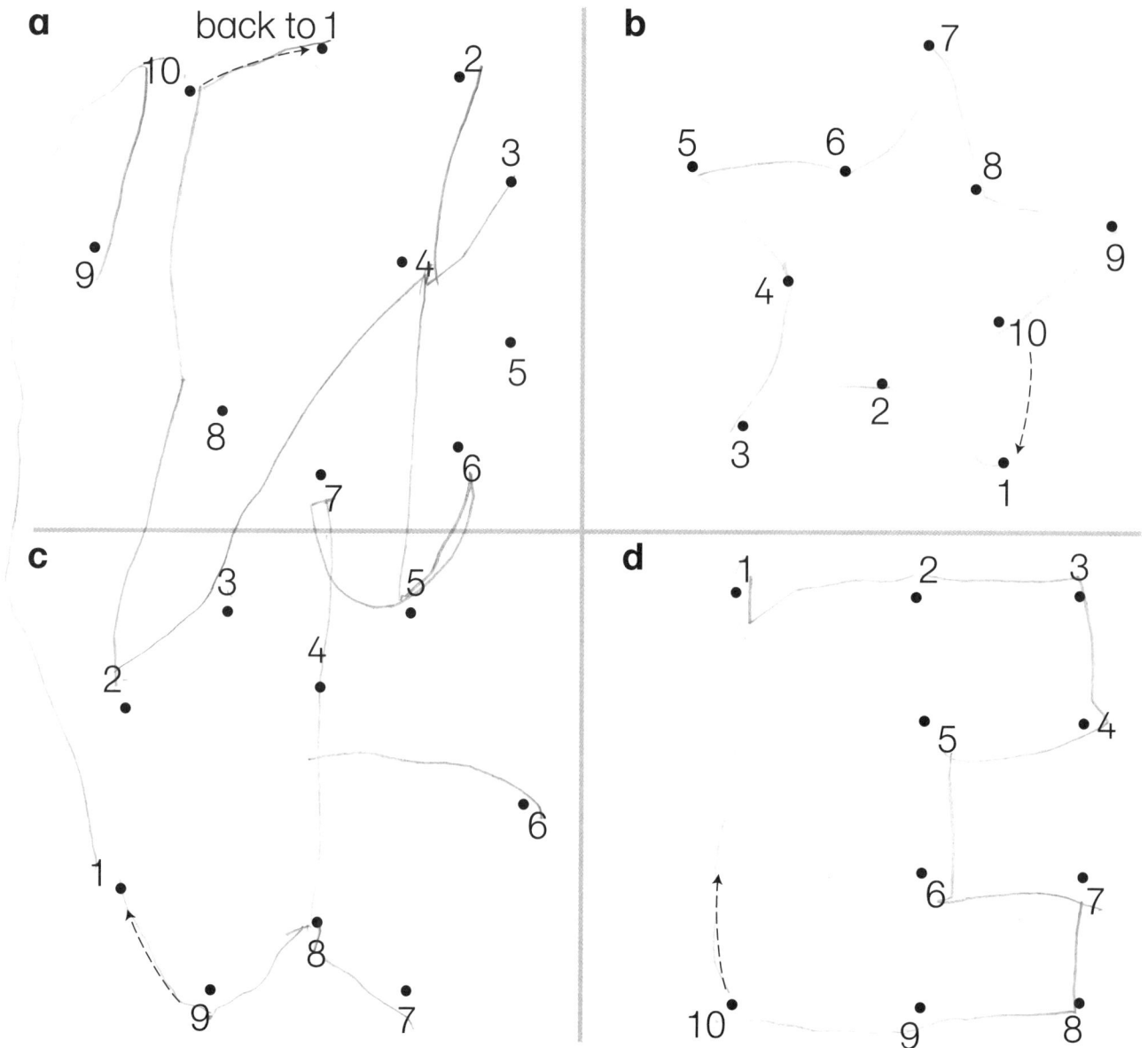

a

b

c

d

2. Fill in the missing numbers.

a 1 2 3 4 5 _6_ 7 8 9 10

b 1 2 3 4 5 6 7 _8_ 9 10

c 1 2 3 _4_ 5 _6_ 7 8 9 10

d _1_ 2 3 4 _5_ 6 7 8 9 10

3. Which number comes first when you count?

a 7 or 6? **_6_**   **b** 4 or 5? _____

c 5 or 6? _____   **d** 7 or 8? _____

e 9 or 8? _____   **f** 9 or 10? _____

1	2	3	4	5	6	7	8	9	10

4.

Look at the number line.

a Which number comes before 7? _____

b Which number comes after 5? _____

c Which number comes after 9? _____

d Which number comes before 2? _____

e Which number comes after 6? _____

f Which number comes before 10? _____

g Which number comes after 1? _____

Addition to 10

Remember, we can add numbers together like this ...

   and      makes

5   **and**   **2**   **makes**   **7**

1. Write the missing numbers.

a      and      makes   _____

b      and      makes   _____

c      and      makes   _____

Now we will use the right signs ... **+** and **=**.

d      **+**      **=**   _____

e      **+**      **=**   _____

2. Write the sums in the gaps.

a [apples] and [apples] makes [apples]

$$\underline{\mathbf{6}} \quad + \quad \underline{\mathbf{4}} \quad = \quad \underline{\mathbf{10}}$$

b [apples] and [apples] makes [apples]

$$\underline{\hspace{2cm}} \quad + \quad \underline{\hspace{2cm}} \quad = \quad \underline{\hspace{2cm}}$$

c [apples] and [apples] makes [apples]

$$\underline{\hspace{2cm}} \quad + \quad \underline{\hspace{2cm}} \quad = \quad \underline{\hspace{2cm}}$$

d [apples] and [apples] makes [apples]

$$\underline{\hspace{2cm}} \quad + \quad \underline{\hspace{2cm}} \quad = \quad \underline{\hspace{2cm}}$$

3. Do these sums.

a $6 + 2 = \underline{\hspace{2cm}}$ **b** $8 + 1 = \underline{\hspace{2cm}}$

c $4 + 5 = \underline{\hspace{2cm}}$ **d** $6 + 4 = \underline{\hspace{2cm}}$

e $7 + 3 = \underline{\hspace{2cm}}$ **f** $7 + 1 = \underline{\hspace{2cm}}$

g $5 + 4 = \underline{\hspace{2cm}}$ **h** $9 + 0 = \underline{\hspace{2cm}}$

Subtraction to 10

I have 6 sweets. Count them.

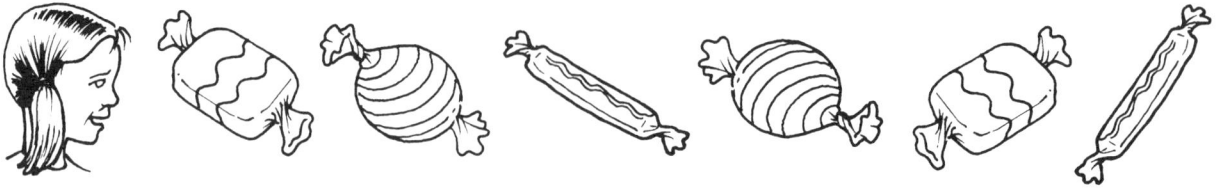

I give 2 to Tom.

I have 4 sweets left.

1. If you take away 2 sweets from each bag how many will you have left?

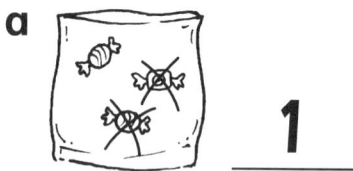

a   **1**

b   _____

c   _____

d   _____

e   _____

f   _____

Now take away 5 sweets.

g   _____

h   _____

i   _____

We write take away sums like this ...

   take away   3   is

7   –   3   =   4

— means take away

2. Write the answers.

a – 2 = _____

b – 5 = _____

c – 4 = _____

d – 6 = _____

3. Finish these sums.
Draw some sweets if it helps.

a 6 – 2 = _____

b 8 – 6 = _____

c 3 – 1 = _____

d 8 – 4 = _____

e 9 – 5 = _____

f 10 – 4 = _____

4. What is the answer?

a 9 take away 5 is _____ .

b If you had 7 pens but lost 3 how many would you have left? _____

c 6 take away 6 is _____ .

Knowing when to add or subtract to 10

Remember ...
+ means **add**
− means **subtract**

1. Answer these sums.

a $6 + 2 =$ _____

b $9 - 3 =$ _____

c $7 - 3 =$ _____

d $8 + 2 =$ _____

e $5 + 4 =$ _____

f $8 - 2 =$ _____

2. Which sign, + or −, makes these sums right? Fill in the gaps.

a 6 _____ $3 = 9$

b 9 _____ $6 = 3$

c 5 _____ $5 = 10$

d 7 _____ $2 = 9$

e 5 _____ $3 = 8$

f 7 _____ $2 = 5$

g 2 _____ $1 = 1$

h 5 _____ $4 = 9$

3. Which sign should you use?

Fill in the gaps with **+** or **−**.

a 6 less 3 = 3

    6 _____ 3 = 3

b 5 subtract 4 = 1

    5 _____ 4 = 1

c 8 and 2 more = 10

    8 _____ 2 = 10

d 2 add 7 = 9

    2 _____ 7 = 9

e 9 take away 7 = 2

    9 _____ 7 = 2

f 7 less 3 = 4

    7 _____ 3 = 4

g 10 subtract 6 = 4

    10 _____ 6 = 4

h 1 and 3 more = 4

    1 _____ 3 = 4

i 6 add 3 = 9

    6 _____ 3 = 9

j 3 take away 3 = 0

    3 _____ 3 = 0

4. Write the right sign in the gap.

a 10p _____ 8p = 2p

b 7p _____ 2p = 9p

c 8p _____ 5p = 3p

d 2p _____ 6p = 8p

e 9p _____ 4p = 5p

First or last, more or less (2)

When something comes **first** it is at the beginning.

When something comes **last** it is at the end.

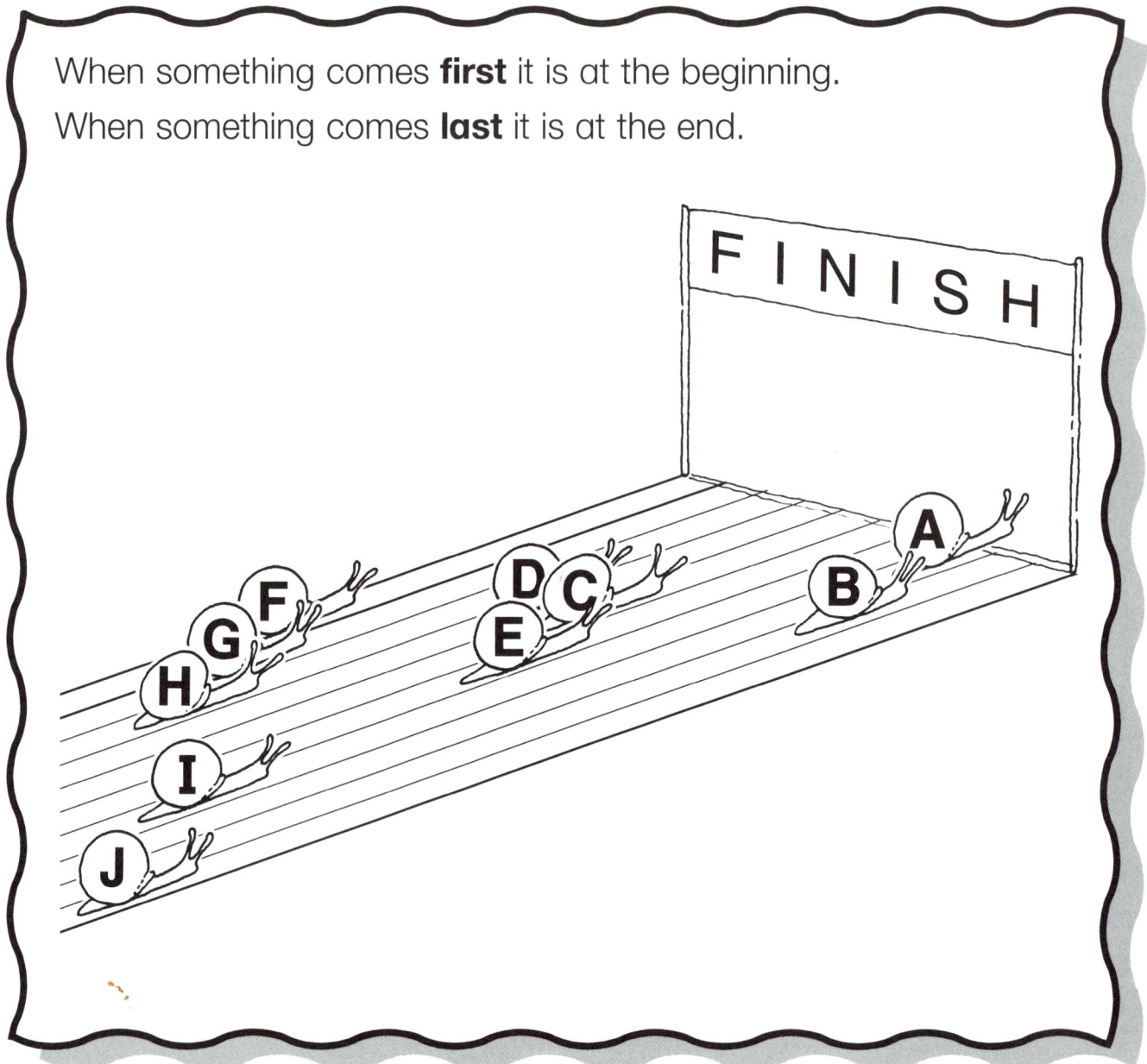

1. Look at the picture. Answer the questions.

a Which snail is last? _____

b Which snail is 2nd? _____

c Which snail is 8th? _____

d Which snail is first? _____

e Which snail is 5th? _____

As numbers go up they are one more than the one before.

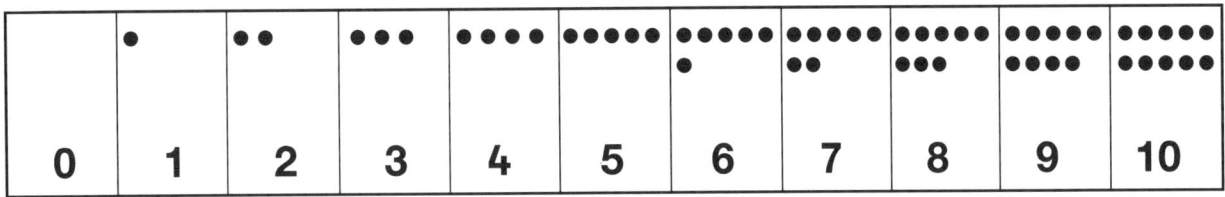

0	1	2	3	4	5	6	7	8	9	10

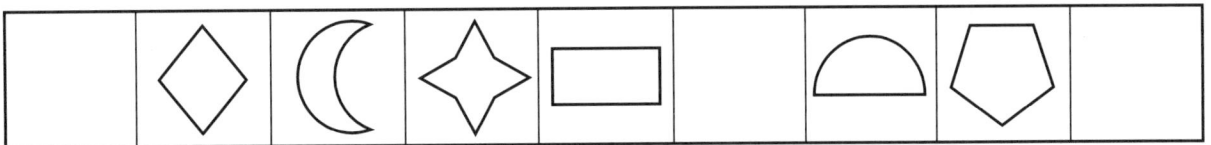

2. Answer these questions about the number line.

a Which numbers are less than 2? _____ _____

b Which numbers are more than 8? _____ _____

c Which numbers are less than 4? _____ _____ _____ _____

d Which number is more than 9? _____

3. Fill in the gaps with shapes. Put them where they need to go.

a Put a △ first.

b Put a ☐ in 6th place.

c Put a ◯ last.

Answer these questions.

d Which shape is 3rd? _____

e Which shape is 8th? _____

f Which shape comes after this shape? _____

Fractions – a half

Look at this cake.

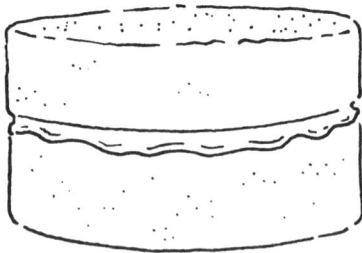 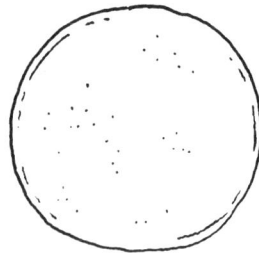

If we cut it into two equal bits, it looks like this ...

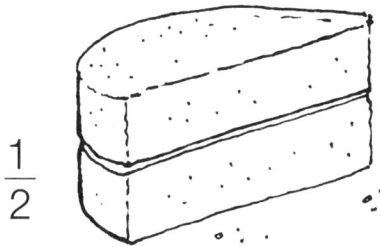  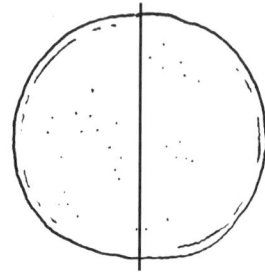

$\frac{1}{2}$ ... $\frac{1}{2}$

We say we have cut it in **half**.

1. Cut these things in half.

a
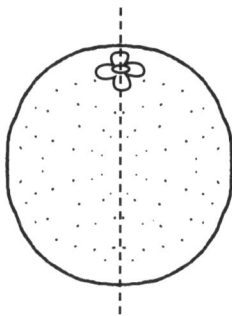

b

c

d

e

f

We write a **half** like this ... $\frac{1}{2}$

2. Now cut these shapes in $\frac{1}{2}$.
Colour one $\frac{1}{2}$ of each shape.

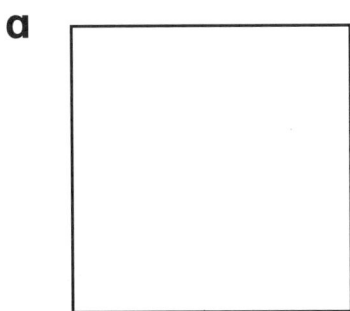

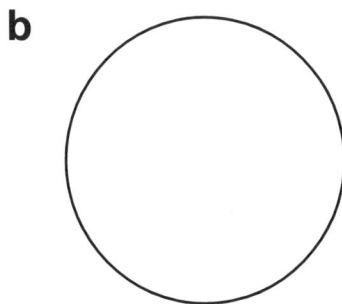

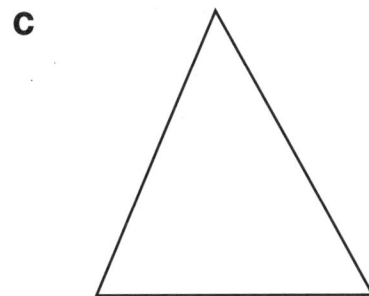

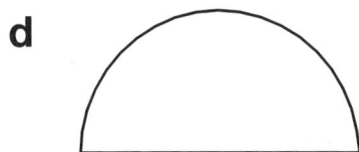

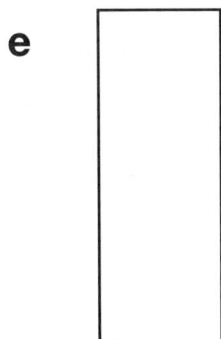

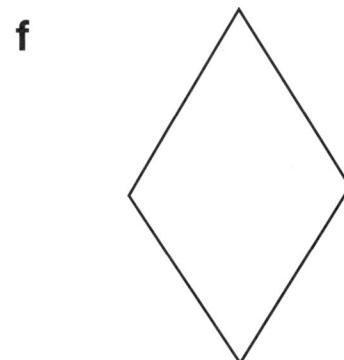

a

b

c

d

e

f

3. Tick the shapes that have been cut in $\frac{1}{2}$.

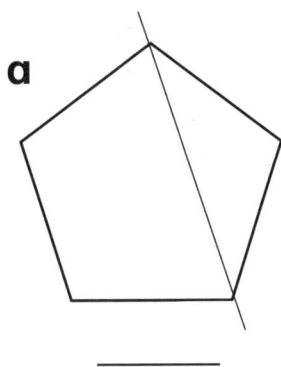

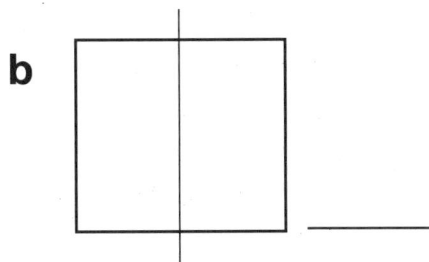

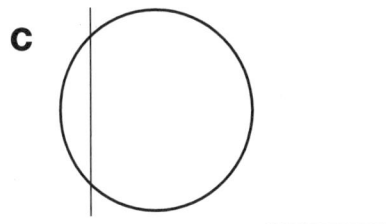

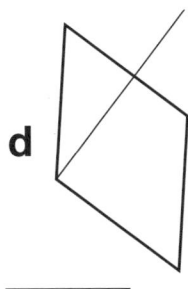

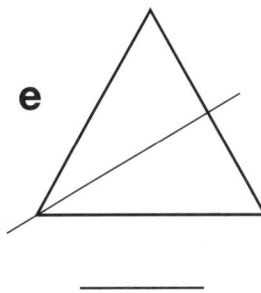

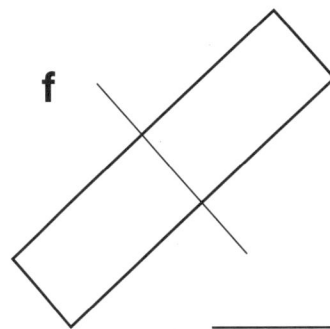

a

b

c

d

e

f

Number sequences

This is a **number line**.

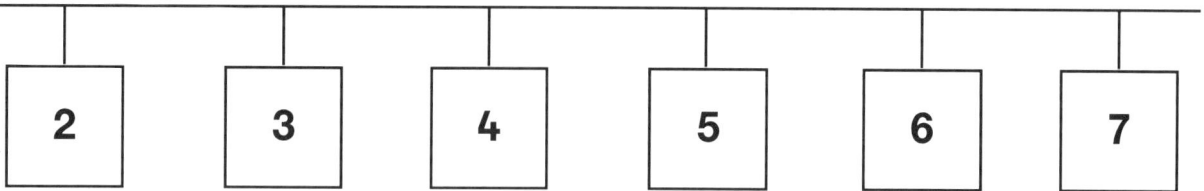

| 2 | 3 | 4 | 5 | 6 | 7 |

The numbers are in order.

1. Fill in the missing numbers.

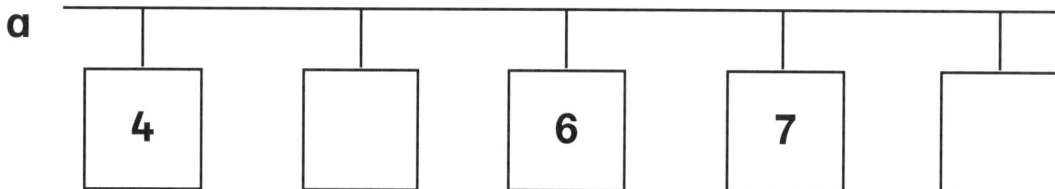

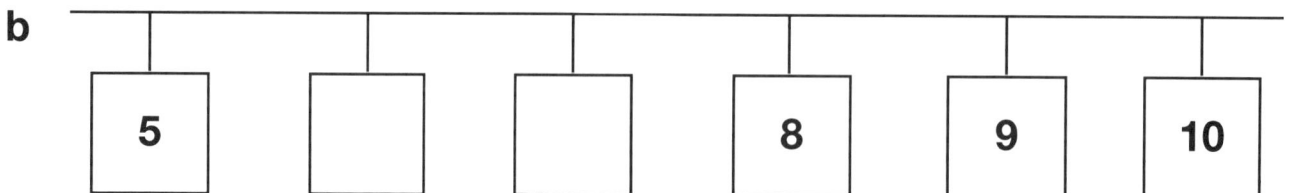

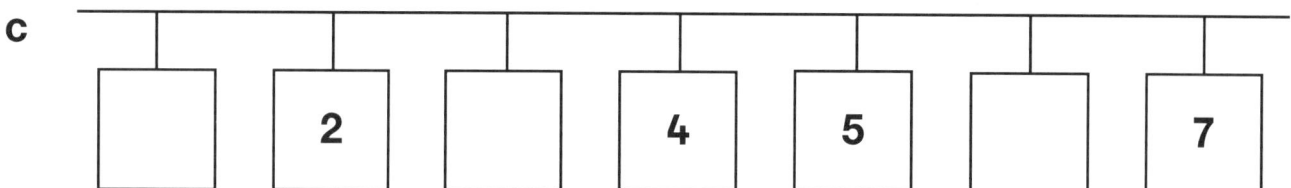

a

| 4 | | 6 | 7 | |

b

| 5 | | | 8 | 9 | 10 |

c

| | 2 | | 4 | 5 | | 7 |

2. Which 2 numbers have been changed over?
Put a circle around them.

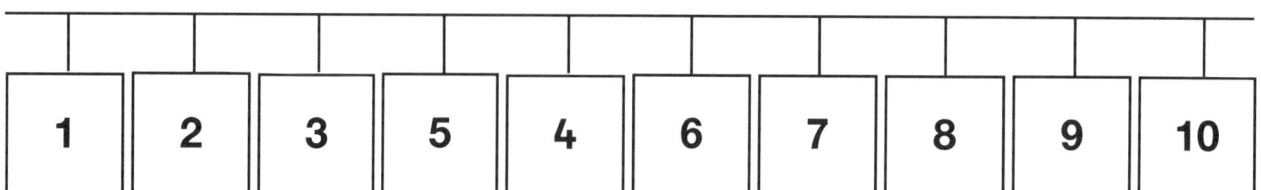

| 1 | 2 | 3 | 5 | 4 | 6 | 7 | 8 | 9 | 10 |

Look carefully at this number line.

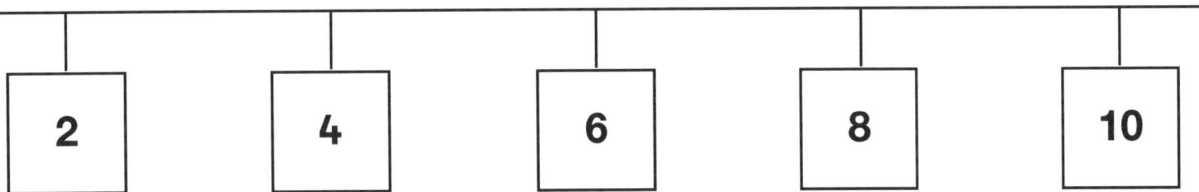

| 2 | 4 | 6 | 8 | 10 |

The numbers go up **2** each time.

3. Fill in the missing numbers.

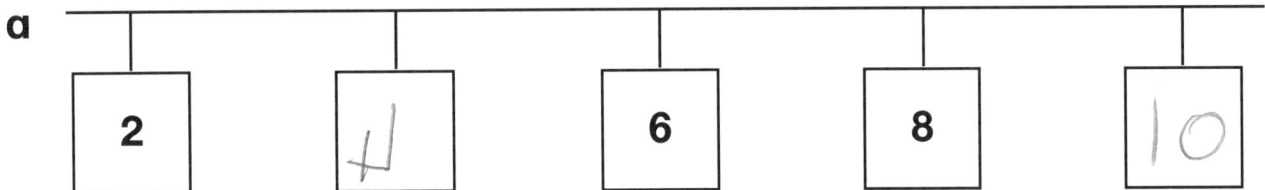

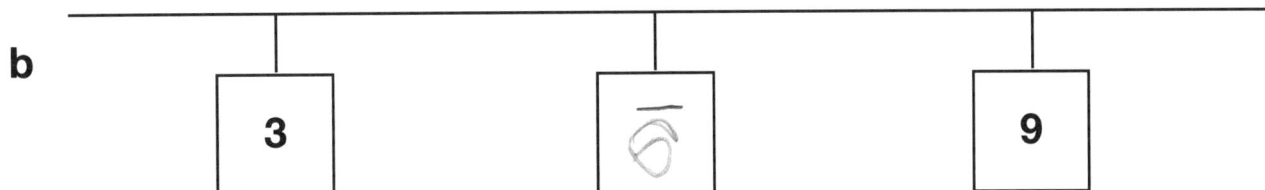

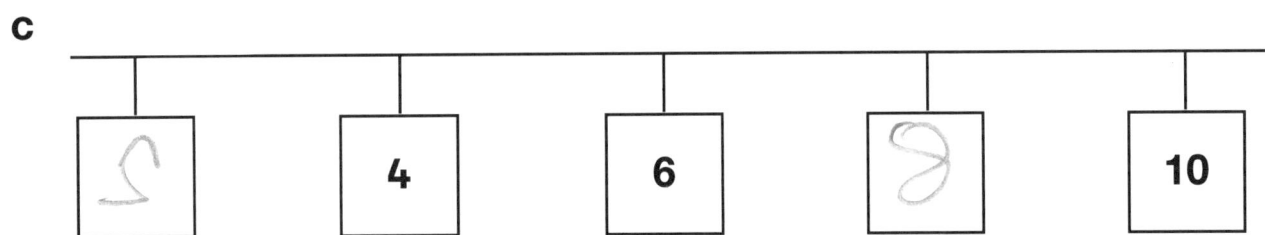

a

| 2 | 4 | 6 | 8 | 10 |

b

| 3 | 6 | 9 |

c

| 2 | 4 | 6 | 8 | 10 |

4. Put these numbers in order, smallest first.

a 6   2   7   10   **2   6   7   10**

b 5   3   9   6   **3** ____ ____ ____

c 7   1   10   8   ____ ____ ____ ____

d 2   5   4   9   ____ ____ ____ ____

Adding to make 10

Look at how many ways we can make 7.

0 + 7 = 7	4 + 3 = 7
1 + 6 = 7	5 + 2 = 7
2 + 5 = 7	6 + 1 = 7
3 + 4 = 7	7 + 0 = 7

1. How many different ways can you make 9?

0   +   9   =   9   5   + _____ =   9

1   + _____ =   9   6   +   3   = _____

_____ +   7   =   9   _____ +   2   =   9

3   +   6   = _____   8   + _____ =   9

_____ +   5   =   9   _____ +   0   =   9

2. How many different ways can you make 4?

_____ +   4   =   4   _____ + _____ =   4

_____ + _____ =   4   _____ + _____ =   4

_____ + _____ =   4

3. Fill in the gaps.

$0 + 0 =$ **0** $3 + 3 =$ _____

$1 + 1 =$ _____ $4 + 4 =$ _____

$2 + 2 =$ _____ $5 + 5 =$ _____

How many does the answer go up each time? _____

4. Tick the answers that are right.

a $6 + 3 = 9$ _____   **b** $7 - 3 = 5$ _____

c $2 + 7 = 10$ _____   **d** $5 + 3 = 8$ _____

e $5 + 5 = 9$ _____   **f** $7 - 4 = 3$ _____

5. Answer these questions.

a There were 8 buttons on a coat.
3 fell off. How many were left? _____

b 5 apples were on the tree. 2 fell off. How many were left? _____

c There were 10 cakes. 3 are eaten. How many are left? _____

d A bag of 7 sweets had a hole in it.
4 sweets fell out. How many were left? _____

Check-up 2

1. How many flowers?

   a   **b**

2. Fill in the missing numbers.

   a 3   4 _____ 6 7 8

   b 7   8 _____ 10

3. Do these sums.

   a $6 + 3 =$ _____   **b** $5 + 5 =$ _____

   c $5 + 1 =$ _____   **d** $6 + 0 =$ _____

4. Do these sums.

   a $8 - 3 =$ _____   **b** $10 - 5 =$ _____

   c $7 - 6 =$ _____   **d** $6 - 4 =$ _____

5. Which sign is missing? Fill in the gaps.

   a 5 _____ 3 = 8   **b** 5 _____ 2 = 3

   c 2 _____ 7 = 9   **d** 7 _____ 3 = 4

6. a Which number comes before 8? _____

   b Which number comes after 3? _____

7. Draw lines to cut these shapes in $\frac{1}{2}$.

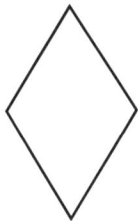  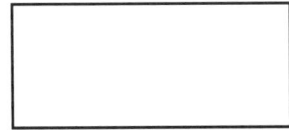

8. Fill in the missing numbers.

a

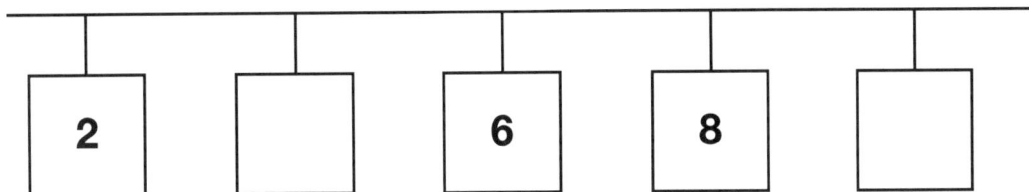

b

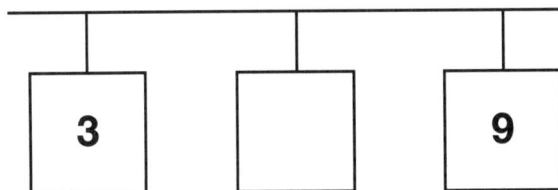

9. Fill in the gaps.

   a 0 + 0 = _____   **b** 3 + 3 = _____

   c 1 + 1 = _____   **d** 4 + 4 = _____

   e 2 + 2 = _____   **f** 5 + 5 = _____

Read and write numbers to 20

1. Colour

    a 9 beads red.   **b** 12 beads green.   **c** 17 beads blue.

2. How many beads on each necklace?

a

b

_____

c

d

_____

3. Put a red circle around each number 18.
Put a green circle around each number 17.
Put a blue circle around each number 20.

12   18   17   5   20   18   17

8   20   18   6   5   20   10   18

16   11   18   17   12   9   20

4. Draw beads on the necklaces.

11 red beads   15 blue beads   17 green beads

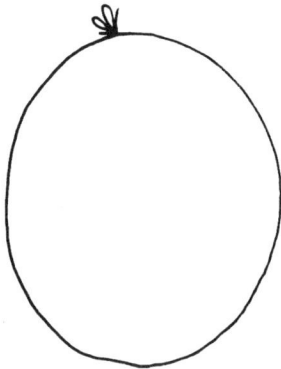

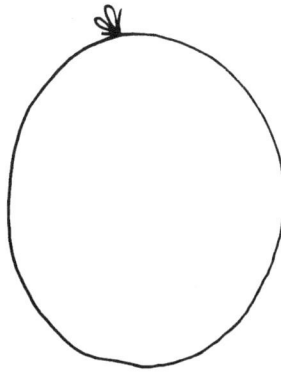

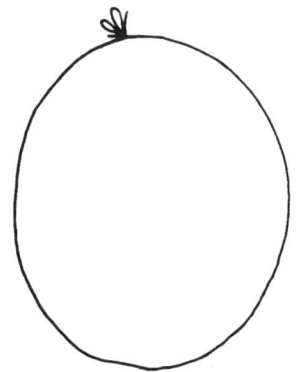

5. Put a tick in each necklace with 13 beads.

Tens and units

Look at the number 14.

14 is **1 ten** and **4 units**

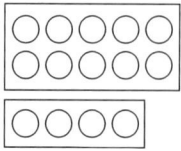

ten

units

1. Fill in the gaps.

a 12 = = _____ ten _____ units

b 18 = = _____ ten _____ units

c 6 = = _____ ten _____ units

d 15 = = _____ ten _____ units

e 11 = = _____ ten _____ units

2. Draw the tens and units and fill in the gaps.

a 14   =   __**1**__ ten   __**4**__ units   =

b 17   =   _____ ten   _____ units   =

c 8   =   _____ ten   _____ units   =

d 13   =   _____ ten   _____ units   =

3. Which number is the same as ...

a one ten and seven units? _____

b one ten and one unit? _____

c no tens and three units? _____

d one ten and nine units? _____

Counting in steps to 20

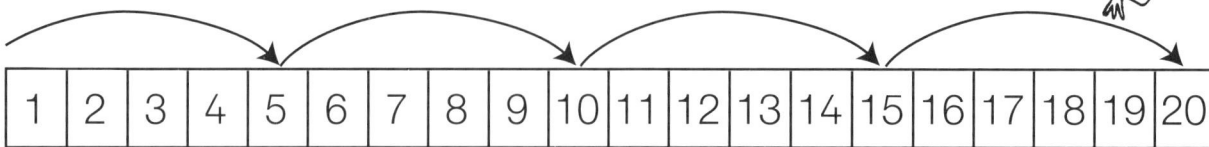

Look at the frog. It is jumping along the number line.

| 1 | 2 | 3 | 4 | 5 | 6 | 7 | 8 | 9 | 10 | 11 | 12 | 13 | 14 | 15 | 16 | 17 | 18 | 19 | 20 |

The frog jumps up **5** numbers each time.

1. How many numbers does the frog jump up each time?

a

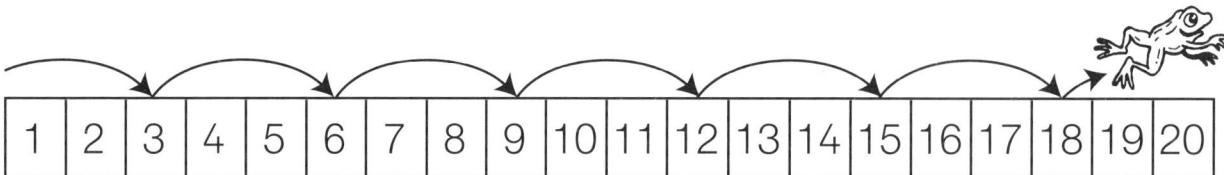

| 1 | 2 | 3 | 4 | 5 | 6 | 7 | 8 | 9 | 10 | 11 | 12 | 13 | 14 | 15 | 16 | 17 | 18 | 19 | 20 |

___**3**___ numbers each time

b

| 1 | 2 | 3 | 4 | 5 | 6 | 7 | 8 | 9 | 10 | 11 | 12 | 13 | 14 | 15 | 16 | 17 | 18 | 19 | 20 |

_____ numbers each time

2. Finish the jumps keeping them the same.

a

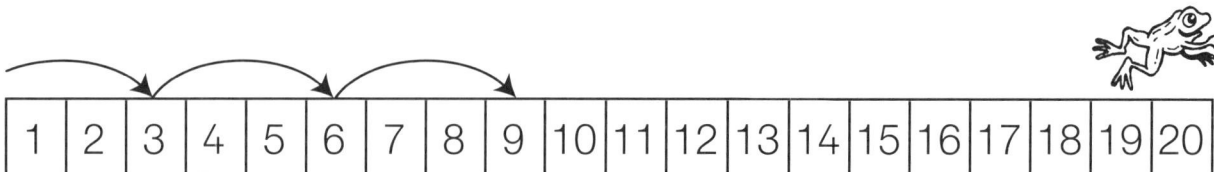

| 1 | 2 | 3 | 4 | 5 | 6 | 7 | 8 | 9 | 10 | 11 | 12 | 13 | 14 | 15 | 16 | 17 | 18 | 19 | 20 |

b

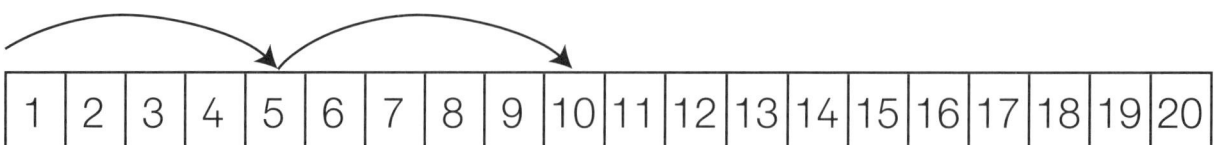

| 1 | 2 | 3 | 4 | 5 | 6 | 7 | 8 | 9 | 10 | 11 | 12 | 13 | 14 | 15 | 16 | 17 | 18 | 19 | 20 |

3. Which numbers come next?

a 3   6   9 _____ _____

b 5   10 _____ _____

c 2   4   6 _____ _____

d 4   8 _____ _____

4. Fill in the missing numbers.

a 6   9 _____ 15

b 2 _____ _____ 8 _____ _____

c 5 _____ 15 _____

5. Colour red the numbers that go up by 2 each time.

1	2	3	4	5
6	7	8	9	10
11	12	13	14	15
16	17	18	19	20

Problems involving measures

The train is **longer** than the car.

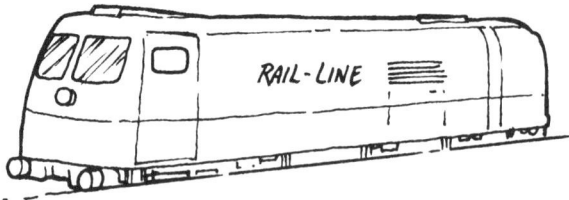 

1. Colour in the longer object.

a     **b**

c

Bob is **taller** than Tom.

Bob   Tom

2. Tick the taller child.

a    **b**    **c**

_____   _____   _____   _____   _____   _____

> The dog is **heavier** than the bird.

3. Colour in the heavier animal.

a

b

c

4.
Dex   Spot

a Which dog has the longer tail? _____

b Which dog is heavier? _____

Time – o'clock

We know what time it is by looking at a clock.

This clock shows
it is **3 o'clock**.

The **big hand** is pointing at the **12**.
The **small hand** is pointing at the **3**.

1. What is the time?

a

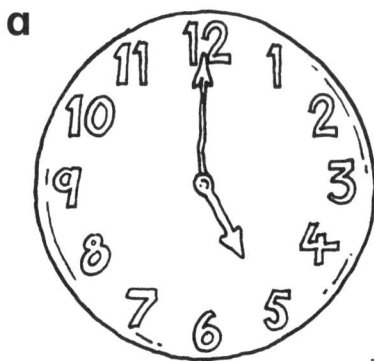

_____ o'clock

b

_____ o'clock

c

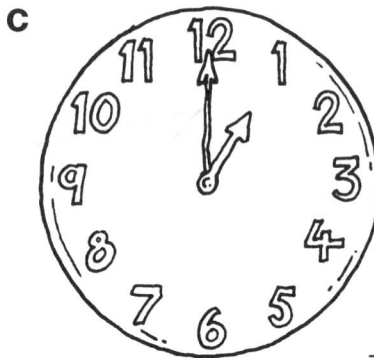

_____ o'clock

d

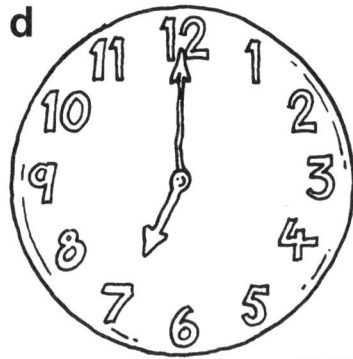

_____ o'clock

2. Draw the small hand on the clocks.

a

3 o'clock

b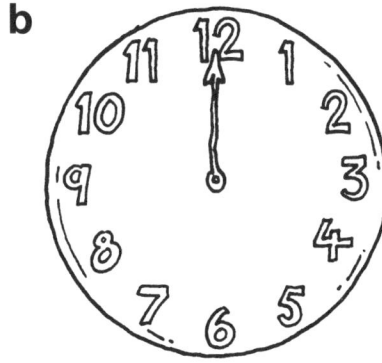

5 o'clock

c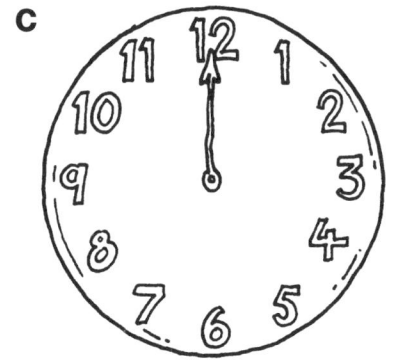

9 o'clock

d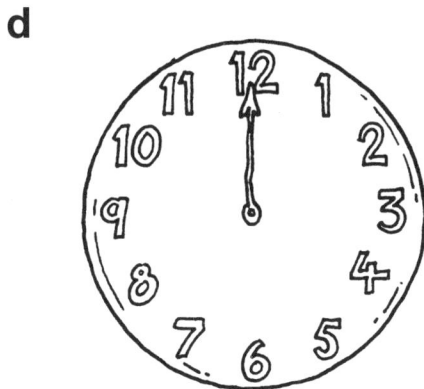

11 o'clock

e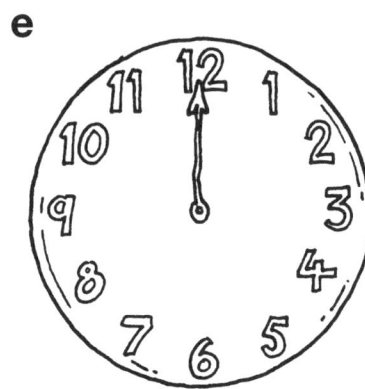

7 o'clock

f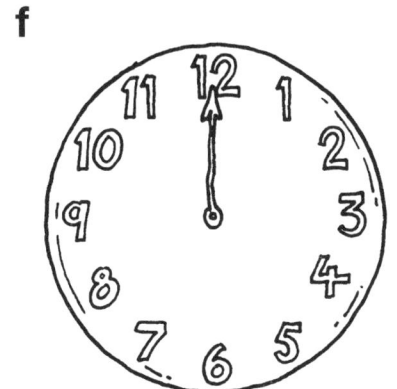

2 o'clock

3. It is 4 o'clock.

a What time will it be in one hour's time? _____

b What time was it 3 hours ago? _____

c In how many hours will it be 6 o'clock? _____

Fractions – a quarter

Look at this cake.

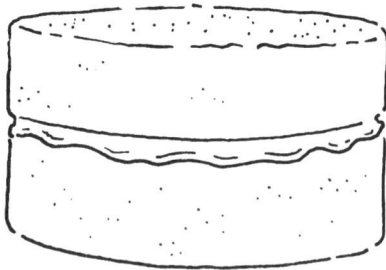

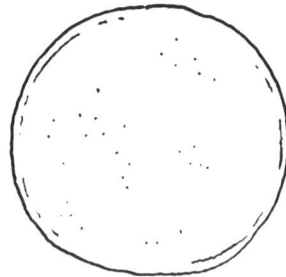

If we cut it into four equal bits it looks like this.

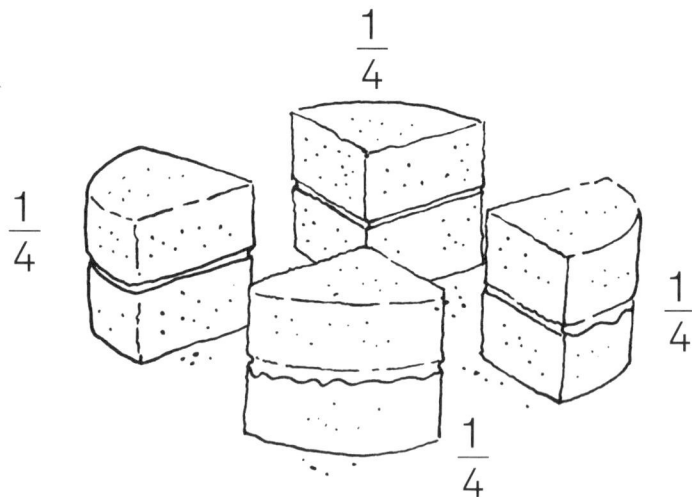

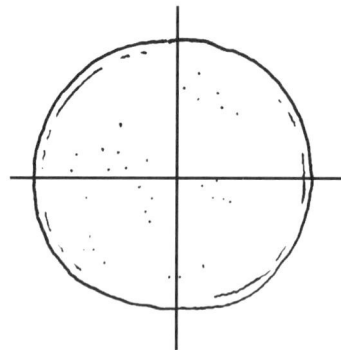

$\frac{1}{4}$

$\frac{1}{4}$

$\frac{1}{4}$

$\frac{1}{4}$

We say we have cut it into **quarters.**

1. Cut these things into quarters.

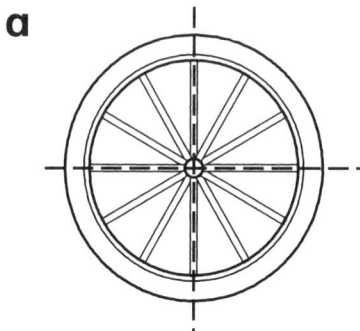

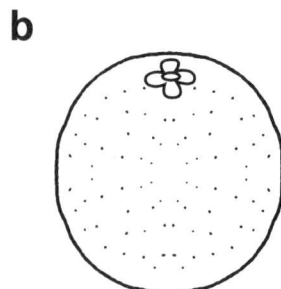

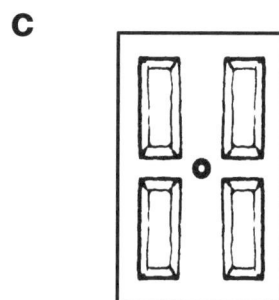

a

b

c

We write a quarter like this ... $\frac{1}{4}$

2. Cut these shapes into $\frac{1}{4}$s.

a
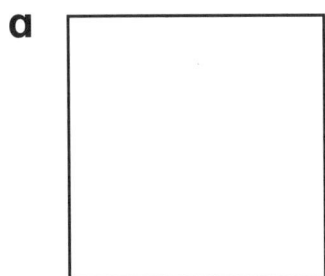

b
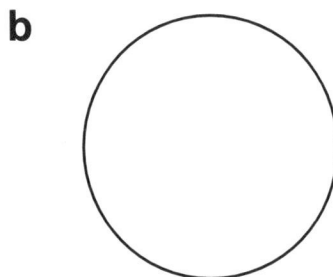

c

d
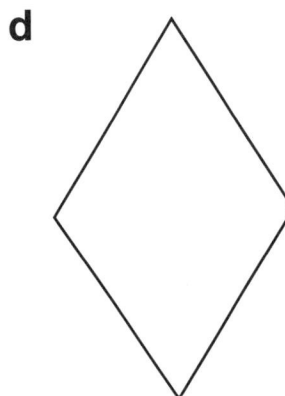

3. Tick the shapes that have been cut into $\frac{1}{4}$s.

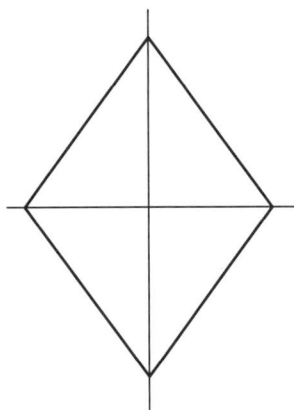
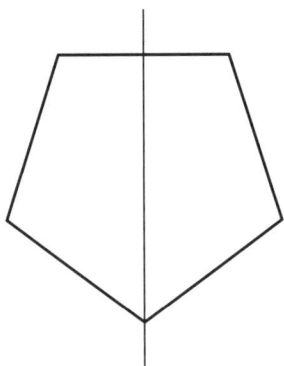
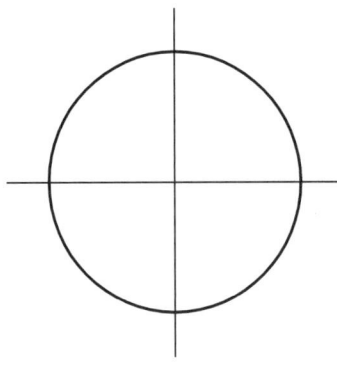
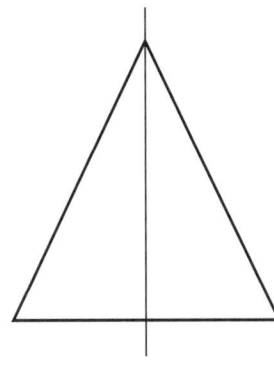

Estimation

1. a Don't count, just guess how many cats there are here. _____

Now count them. _____

b Don't count, just guess how many dogs there are here. _____

Now count them. _____

c Guess how many birds there are here. _____

Now count them. _____

Another way of saying 'guess how many' is **'estimate** how many'.

2. Make your estimation and count only to check your answers.

    a Estimate how many ducks are in the pond.   _____

    b Estimate how many chickens are in the pen.   _____

    c Estimate how many cows are in the field.   _____

    d Estimate how many ladybirds are in the jar.   _____

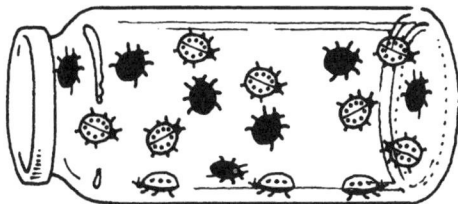

3. Estimate whether there are enough apples for the donkeys to have one each. Put a circle around 'Yes' or 'No'.

Yes   No

3D shapes

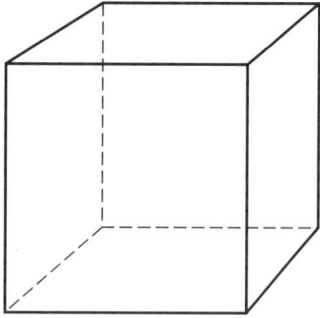

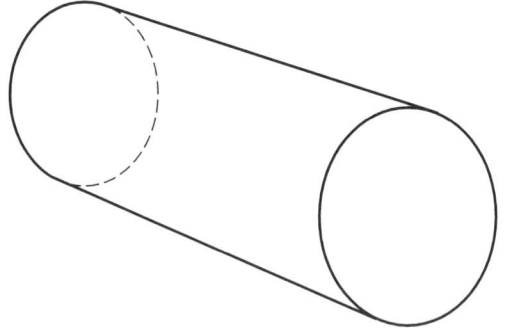

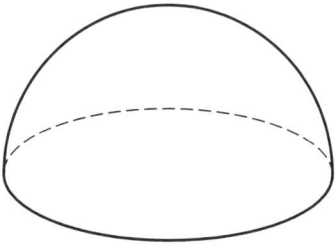

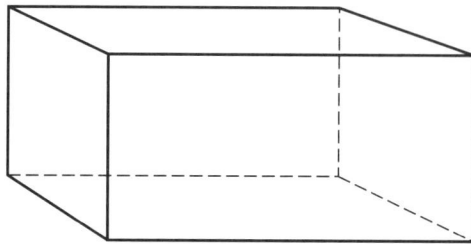

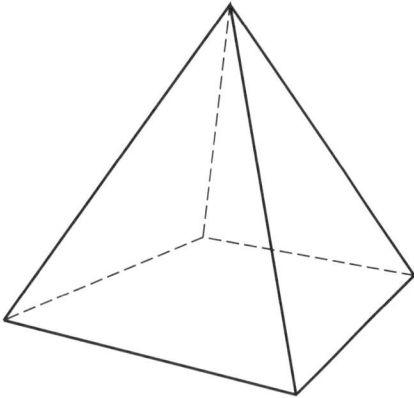

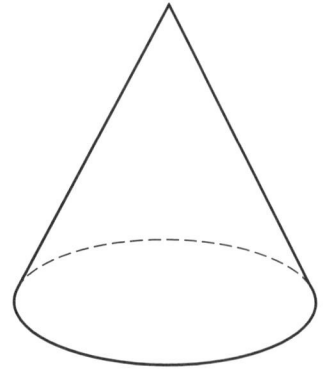

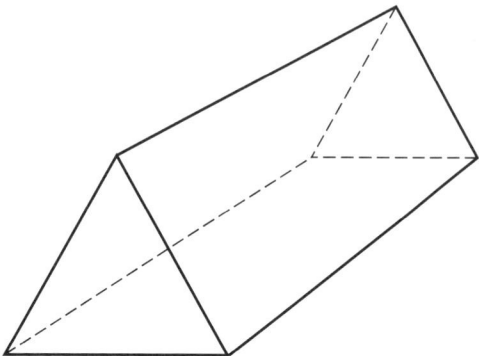

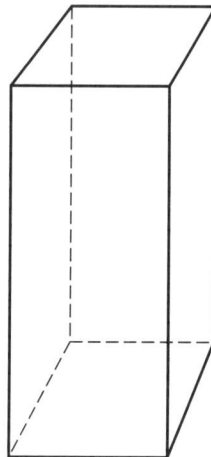

1. Look at page 60.

   a Colour blue the shapes that can roll.

   b How many shapes have one or more points? _____

   c Put a circle around the shapes that have flat sides.

2. How many flat sides do these shapes have?

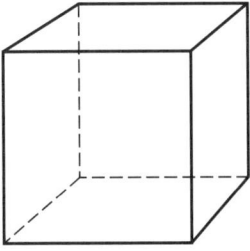

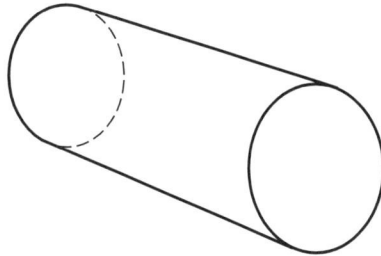

cube   **cylinder**

_____ flat sides   _____ flat sides

3. Look at these shapes.

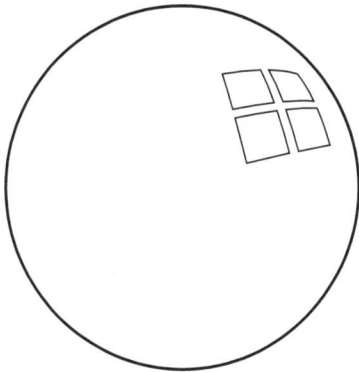

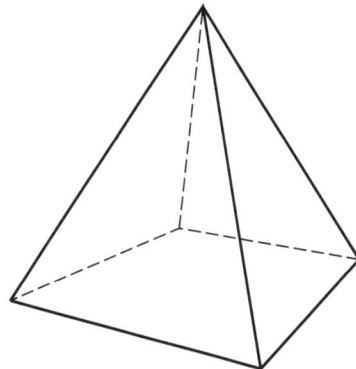

sphere   **pyramid**

Write the names of the shapes in the gaps.

   a The _____ can roll.

   b The _____ has a point.

   c The _____ has flat sides.

Odd and even numbers (to 10)

Look at these numbers.

1   3   5   7   9

The first number is 1. The numbers go up two at a time.

These are **odd** numbers.

Look at these numbers.

2   4   6   8   10

The first number is 2. The numbers go up two at a time.

These are **even** numbers.

1. a What is the first odd number? _____

  b What is the second even number? _____

  c What is the third odd number? _____

  d What is the first even number? _____

  e What is the fifth odd number? _____

If a number can be split exactly in two it is an **even** number.

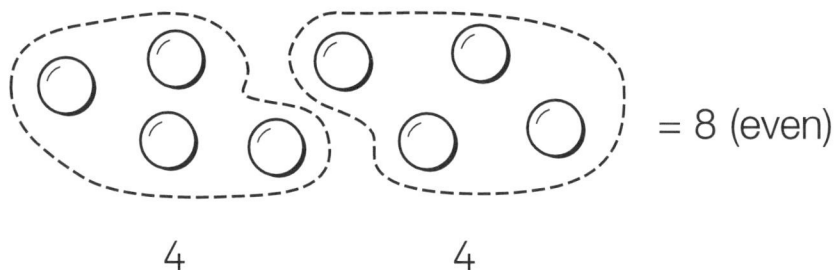

4   4   = 8 (even)

If a number cannot be split exactly in two it is an **odd** number.

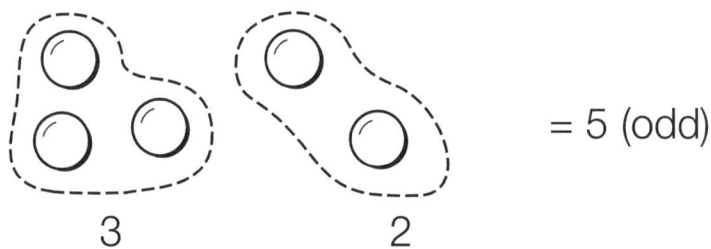

3   2   = 5 (odd)

2. Are these numbers odd or even?

a 6 = = **even**

b 3 = = _____

c 5 = = _____

d 9 = = _____

e 8 = = _____

f 4 = = _____

3. a Colour the even numbers red.

b Colour the odd numbers green.

1	2	3	4	5	6	7	8	9	10

Test yourself

1. How many fish in the bowl?

_____

2. Which number comes after 4?

_____

Which number comes before 2?

_____

3. 4 + 1 = _____

4. 5 − 3 = _____

5. 4 _____ 2 = 2

6. Which number is less than 2?

_____

7. Make 3 in two different ways.

___ + ___ = 3

___ + ___ = 3

8. How many sides does a square have?

_____

How many sides does a triangle have?

_____

9. Finish the pattern.

| ✗ | ○ | ○ | ✗ | | |

10. Put a line around the day that comes after Monday.

Thursday   Tuesday

11. Colour 7 flowers.

12. Which number comes before 7?

_____

Which number comes after 9?

_____